The Swarm

Martyn Beardsley ✳ Jonatronix

OXFORD
UNIVERSITY PRESS

From: STING, Charles
To: Top secret

Subject: TEAM X

📎 Villain profile: the Collector

To *******

Following the arrest of Dr X, we have made several changes
at NICE.

- NICE is now the *National Institute for the Conservation of Earth.*
- Dani Day has been appointed to the position of Senior Scientist.
- The mission of NICE is to help protect the planet and the
  precious things in it.

In order to help NICE in its mission, Dani Day has employed a
team of four agents. She assures me that they are highly capable.
In order to protect the agents, their real identities must remain a
secret. They have been given the name Team X. Their operation
status is now **code green**.

Team X have been monitoring a new villain. He calls himself the
Collector. The Collector is known to have carried out some serious
crimes [see file attached].

I will keep you informed of any further changes.

Regards

Charles I. Sting
**Director of Operations,
NICE**

Important
Agent Information
Read this first

Villain profile: the Collector

Threat category: High

Known crimes:
- Theft of the entire population of cod in the North Atlantic.
- Theft of the White Cliffs of Dover.
- Attempted theft of the Sphinx at Giza. The robbery failed, but he did get away with the Sphinx's nose.

Appearance:
Dark hair. Brown Eyes. 182 centimetres tall. Snappy dresser. Bionic hand. Spectrum retina enhanced implant.

Profile:
The Collector is a billionaire. How he made his fortune is not known. His goal is to own the biggest collection of snow globes in the world. Using advanced micro science he shrinks and steals valuable objects. No target is too big. He does not care about the consequences of his actions.

Other things to note:
He likes to send snow globes to taunt his victims.

TEAM X DESTINATION: SAHARA DESERT

Continent: Africa
Country: Tunisia
Destination: Sahara Desert
Climate: Hot, dry desert, rain is rare

The Sahara Desert is the world's largest hot desert. It spans 13 countries and covers most of Northern Africa – approximately 9 000 000 square kilometres – which makes it almost as large as the whole of Europe!

Chapter 1 – The empty hive

Rita Motherwell had been a bee keeper all her life. She *knew* bees. She knew their flight patterns. She knew about the different buzzing sounds and what they meant. She knew about how to extract honey and how to make beeswax candles. And she knew about what to put on bee stings to make them better. What she did *not* know was what was happening to her bees right now.

As soon as she walked out into the field where she kept her hives, she spotted that something was wrong. Very wrong. She lifted the veil on the hood of her white bee-keeper's jacket.

"What's going on?" she said, out loud.

All her bees were flying out of their hives. They were funnelling upwards, forming a thick black cloud. The air was filled with a rhythmical buzzing. The swarm circled once, then soared into the sky and headed south. Moments later, they were gone.

Rita heard a voice behind her. She turned to see four children.

"Whoa, look at that!" said Tiger, staring up into the sky.

"Tiger," whispered Ant. "Your watch …"

Tiger looked at his wrist. His watch was flashing a red X-bot alert.

"Eyes peeled, Team X," whispered Max, quietly.

"What are you doing here?" snapped Rita. "This is private land!"

"Sorry," Cat replied, nervously. "We just saw all the bees fly away and ..."

"No, I'm sorry," interrupted Rita, "I shouldn't have shouted. It's just that my bees … they've all gone!"

"Is that unusual?" said Max. "For them to fly off like that, I mean?"

"Very." Rita took off her thick leather glove and wiped her eyes. "I know this will sound stupid, but it was as if they were hypnotized."

"We know some people who might be able to help," said Tiger.

But Rita was not listening. Instead she was gazing sadly at the distant sky.

"Come on," said Max, to the others. "Let's get back to NICE and report to Dani." He was determined to get to the bottom of this.

Together, the children headed back to the X-gate.

Chapter 2 – The breakthrough

"Is that another hive gone?" asked Dani, when the children were back at NICE.

"I'm afraid so," replied Max.

"That's the fifth report today. Plus the three yesterday." Dani tapped away at her keyboard. A map of the world appeared. "I've had reports from agents in Luxemburg, Poland, China, the USA, and New Zealand. They all say the same thing. Bees are disappearing everywhere. Here, have a look at this," said Dani, handing Cat a newspaper.

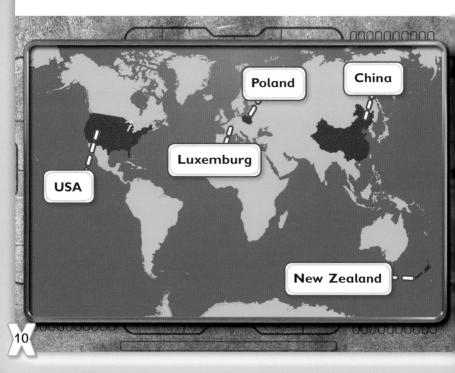

GREENVILLE NEWS

What Can The Matter Bee?

Today the science world is buzzing with speculation. Swarms of bees all over the world are disappearing and nobody seems to know why. The disappearance of bee colonies may not just mean the end of honey production everywhere, but the very end of life itself!

The famous physicist, Albert Einstein, warned that if bees disappeared from the planet then humans would be extinct within four years! When bees fly from plant to plant to collect nectar, they spread pollen. This fertilizes plants. No bees means no more plants, no more food and no more us!

Dani looked up from the computer screen. "I don't know what's happening, but it's up to us to find out."

At that moment, the intercom buzzed. It was the reception desk in the main NICE building. A woman's voice crackled over the speaker.

"Dani, there's been a package delivered for you."

"Funny," said Dani. "I'm not expecting anything."

"I'll go!" cried Tiger, already running towards the door. He was soon back, carrying a parcel wrapped in brown paper. It had a black and yellow ribbon tied round it.

Dani carefully opened the package. Inside, amongst the protective foam, was a snow globe. There was also a note.

Take care of this precious little creature. It might soon be the only one left in the whole world!

"A bee!" gasped Cat.

"So the Collector is behind the missing colonies," growled Tiger.

"It looks like it," sighed Dani, putting the snow globe on the desk.

The Collector was a master criminal with one goal – to own the biggest collection of snow globes in the world. Using advanced micro science, he was able to shrink and steal valuable objects. No target was too big for him. He did not care about the consequences of his actions. In fact, the more mischief and mayhem he caused, the better he liked it. It was up to Team X to stop him.

"But where's he taking the bees?" asked Max.

Ant picked the globe up and turned it gently round in his hands.

"Hmmm …" he muttered to himself. "Hang on, this is not a snow globe …"

"What?" said Tiger, peering over Ant's shoulder.

"It's a *sand* globe. There's sand in here. It's a clue."

"You think the Collector is taking the bees to a beach?" snorted Cat.

"Or … a desert," said Max.

"Well done, Team X!" said Dani. "We have a lead."

Chapter 3 – The next day ...

Dani was staring at the computer screen when Team X entered. She had worked long into the night. She looked exhausted.

"Have you come up with anything, Dani?" said Tiger, who was keen to be out on their next mission.

Dani smiled at the children.

"You've found them, haven't you?" said Cat. "The bees?"

"Possibly," said Dani. "I've been looking at satellite images of all the major deserts in the world. I wanted to see if there's been any unusual activity. I noticed something odd happening over the Sahara Desert." Dani pointed to the map.

"What?" asked Max.

"Clouds," she replied.

"Clouds?" said Tiger. "What's weird about that?"

"These were black clouds. Lots of them."

"And?"

"Black clouds normally mean rain. It hardly ever rains in the desert."

Max was busy studying the swirling satellite images on the screen. "So you think the clouds are the swarms of bees?"

"Exactly," said Dani.

"Great, let's go!" said Cat, turning towards the X-gate teleport.

The X-gate teleport allowed the children to get anywhere in the world in seconds.

"Not so fast," ordered Dani.

"What is it?" asked Tiger. "Aren't we going to rescue the bees?"

"Yes," replied Dani. "I want you to go and find out what's going on. We need to know how the Collector is getting all the bees to fly to one place."

"So what's the problem?" asked Ant.

"I've got to show you your new machines first!" said Dani, with a grin.

"New machines!" exclaimed Tiger, his eyes lighting up with excitement. "Now you're talking!"

Dani led the children across the room. She pushed a button on the wall. There was a hissing sound and a square door in the middle of the wall began to slide upwards.

The children all gasped.

"Wow!" said Ant. "Bee-machines!"

Dani gently lifted out each machine in turn and handed them to the children. "It took me most of the night to get them right." Dani allowed herself a flash of pride.

"They're amazing," said Ant, looking at the detail.

"They look a lot safer than your old micro-copter," said Cat, looking at Max. She still shivered every time she thought about going up in Max's homemade flying machine.

"They will help you to get close to the bees," said Dani. "Not too close though!" she warned.

Team X carefully inspected their new bee-machines while Dani prepared the X-gate teleport. She walked over to the teleport launch pad and typed in the coordinates. The X-gate shimmered into existence.

"The bee-machines are easy to operate," Dani said, "and you'll be able to talk to each other, so make sure you work together. I'll be tracking you all the way. Good luck!" she said, finally.

"We'll do our best," promised Max.

Carefully holding their new bee-machines, one by one, the children leaped into the centre of the X-gate and disappeared.

Chapter 4 – The super hive

The children stepped out of the X-gate into the African sunshine.

"The Sahara Desert!" exclaimed Ant, blinking in wonder.

Around them was a golden-yellow landscape that shimmered in the heat.

Tiger shielded his eyes. "But where are the bees?" he asked, looking up.

At that moment, the sky filled with a distant humming sound. A dark cloud blotted out the sun.

"Bees!" said Max. "Come on. Let's shrink so we can follow them."

They turned the dials on their special watches anticlockwise. A bright blue X appeared in the centre of each one. They pushed the X and in an instant, the team were micro-sized.

Max, Cat, Ant and Tiger climbed into their bee-machines and strapped themselves in. The controls were easy to figure out. The start button set the rotor blades spinning and lifted the machine into the air. A double joystick steered the machine. Each of the children had a helmet and a headset which meant that they could keep in contact with each other.

Max pulled the mouthpiece down into position. "Ready for take off?"

"Wait!" said Tiger, excitedly. "Can we all have code names, like in the movies … like Red Leader One?"

"Tiger," said Max, sternly. "We really don't have time for this!"

"Oh, *please?*"

Max sighed. "OK," he said. "We'll use the colours of our watches. Ant, you can be *Green Grass One*. Cat, you're *Yellow Desert Two*, I'll be *Blue Sky Three*. And Tiger …"

"Yes?"

"You can be *Red Sunset Four.*"

Tiger groaned. "That's not very exciting."

"Tiger, the bees will be disappearing into the sunset if we don't get going," said Cat.

They all pushed their start buttons and the four bee-machines lifted into the air.

The children followed the swarm in their bee-machines, staying at a safe distance. They flew on and on over the sand dunes.

"This place goes on for ever!" said Tiger.

"The desert is almost the size of the USA," said Ant. "So if the Collector is trying to hide something, this is the place to do it."

A shape came into view on the horizon.

"What's that?" gasped Cat. She thought her eyes were playing tricks on her in the heat.

As they got closer, they could make out a massive building. It looked like a wooden skyscraper split into sections.

Black clouds of bees filled the sky as swarms poured in from all directions, twisting and turning, flowing downwards, towards it.

"It's a giant hive," said Max, in alarm. "A *super* hive!"

Chapter 5 – The deadly dance

The sky darkened with bees as the children got closer to the super hive. The noise of humming was intense.

"There are thousands of them!" exclaimed Cat, above the noise.

"Millions, more like," said Ant. "And they all seem to know what they are doing."

"They work as a team," said Max, who had been reading up on bees. "There are the drones, workers and queen bees. And then there are the guards, whose job it is to protect the hive against intruders."

Tiger looked down at his watch. It had suddenly begun to flash a red warning signal.

"Blue Sky Three," said Tiger, urgently. "Emergency! I repeat, emergency!"

"What is it, Tig … Red Sunset Four?" Max asked quickly.

"X-bot alert."

"X-bots! Keep your eyes open," instructed Max.

Just then, Ant peeled away from the rest of the team. He had seen a strange-looking bee up ahead.

"Where are you going, Green Grass One?" yelled Max. But Ant didn't answer. Max turned his craft in. "After him!"

Max, Cat and Tiger charged after Ant. He was heading to the front of the swarm. They dodged round, over and under hundreds of drone and worker bees. Finally they caught up with Ant who was hovering underneath the swarm near the front. Now they could see what he was looking at.

"It's an X-bot bee!" cried Tiger.

The swarm came to a sudden stop in front of the X-bot bee. Team X watched as the X-bot made a complicated series of movements. Ant filmed it, using the camera on his watch.

"What's it doing?" asked Cat.

"I think it's a waggle dance," replied Max.

"A *what* dance?" asked Tiger. "Why would the Collector teach his X-bots to *dance?*"

"It's no ordinary dance," Max explained. "The waggle dance is what a bee does when it's found a good source of pollen. The pattern the bee makes as it moves around the hive gives the other bees the directions they need to set off and find it."

"Oh," said Tiger.

"But," Max added, grimly, "sometimes it's used for another purpose … to give the bees the directions to a new home."

"So the X-bot bees have been leading all the swarms back to this super hive. But why?" asked Cat.

"I've got it!" said Ant. "If the Collector can get all the bees in the world in one place then he can shrink the lot in one go! Trying to collect each hive in turn would take years, so he's getting them to come here."

The X-bot bee stopped its dance. Then it dropped down towards the super hive.

"Uh, oh," said Ant.

"What is it?" yelled Cat.

At that moment the swarm turned in one mass movement and dived straight down after the X-bot bee. The children were trapped amongst the diving bodies.

"Arggghhhh!" they screamed, as they were pushed downwards towards the super hive.

Chapter 6 – Attack of the guards!

The children in their bee-machines tumbled downwards, out of control. They got nearer and nearer to the super hive. The entrance at the top of the hive looked tiny. Lots and lots of bees were trying to squeeze into the small opening.

"We're going to crash!" shouted Cat.

"Just hold on!" replied Max.

As they reached the giant wooden hive, the bees flew skilfully in through a hole in the top of it. The children were swept into the hive amongst the sea of bees.

Max, Ant and Tiger managed to level out their bee-machines and regain control. But Cat clipped the lip of the entrance with the side of her bee-machine as she entered. She was sent spinning and wobbling at high speed into the dark hive. Quickly, she jerked the joystick back, but this set her on a collision course straight towards the wall of the hive.

"Cat!" cried Tiger, zooming after her.

Cat pulled again on the controls. It was no good. She thought she was going to crash. But, just then, Tiger swooped in beside her. Cat felt her craft knocked to one side, clear of the wall. The movement helped to slow her down. She levelled up and took control of her bee-machine.

Max and Ant flew over.

"You OK, Cat?" asked Max, quickly.

"I … I think so," Cat stammered.

"Nice flying, Tiger," said Ant.

But they did not have time to rest. The buzzing noise inside the hive began to increase.

"I can hardly think!" complained Ant.

"Concentrate, Team X," said Max. "We've got a mission to complete!"

"How're we going to get the bees out?" asked Cat.

"We'll have to do our own waggle dance," said Max.

"A waggle dance!" scoffed Tiger. "I don't know how to *waggle dance!* Don't you need classes or something to learn how to dance?"

"Don't worry," said Ant. "I filmed the X-bot's moves, remember? I thought it would be useful evidence for Dani. Maybe I can reprogramme the moves into our bee-machines."

"Great thinking, Ant," said Max. "Get to work!"

Ant felt around underneath the dashboard until he found the lever he was looking for. He pulled it and a small control panel opened out in front of him. Then Ant replayed the footage of the X-bot bee's waggle dance. He began to type rapidly.

While Ant was working, Max told the others the plan. There were four levels to the super hive. Max reasoned that if they each did a waggle dance on a different level they should be able to lead all of the bees out.

Cat struggled to hear what Max was saying. "What's that noise?" she said, covering her ears.

It was like the buzzing noise of the bees, but more metallic. More machine-like.

Max looked up. "X-bots!" he shouted.

Hurtling towards the children were four X-bot guard bees. They were bigger than the ones they had seen earlier, with vicious looking metal stings that crackled with electric-blue energy.

"They know we're intruders," said Max. "Scatter!"

The children went in different directions. The X-bot guards split up, too.

Max knew they needed extra help. "Dani! Dani!" he shouted, into his watch.

A second later and a fuzzy image of Dani appeared as a hologram out of Max's watch.

"The signal … bad … you're breaking u …" her voice crackled.

"We've got X-bot bees on our tails," said Max. "They have stings! What can we do?"

"Don't let the … touch you. Their stings could knock out your … machines," said Dani, hurriedly. "Use the buttons on the control …"

Then Dani was gone. They were on their own.

Team X sped away from the guard bees. The hive was thronging with so many real bees that the guards seemed confused at first. Max steered his machine to the bottom level of the hive. Cat took the second level, Tiger the third and Ant stayed at the top.

"How are you doing with the waggle dance, Ant?" shouted Max.

"Done!" replied Ant. "I'm sending the moves through to your machines now!"

The control panels in the other three bee-machines automatically opened and the instructions were programmed in.

Max told the others about the extra buttons Dani had mentioned.

"Pollen spray," said Tiger. "What's that?"

There were other buttons too, but Max warned them not to try the buttons until they had to.

There was so much noise and confusion in the crowded hive that Max couldn't be sure if the guard was still on his tail. But then he saw it – heading right for him.

Max held his breath, waited until the guard was almost on him, then dodged left, then right. He circled, twisted and ducked trying to shake the guard, but the X-bot stayed with him.

The X-bot sped up behind him. It held its tail in a stinging position. A crackle of blue electricity came off the sting. Max jabbed the button marked *pollen spray*. A cloud of dust shot out from a tube in the back of his machine. The X-bot guard was covered in a thick fog of pollen. It could not see and went spinning and twisting into the side of the hive. *CRASH!*

"It worked!" Max cried.

Max started the waggle dance and the bee-machine went on to auto pilot. It began dancing round the hive. Slowly the real bees began to take notice.

"Team X, report in …" said Max.

Cat's voice came through his earpiece first. "Yellow Desert Two, reporting … one X-bot guard down!" said Cat, proudly. "I pushed a button that said *nectar collector*. It covered the X-bot in a spray. Loads of real bees came charging towards it. It must have smelt of nectar. The X-bot didn't stand a chance!"

"Well done, Cat," congratulated Max.

"Tiger?"

"Same for me," said Tiger. "I hit the *pure gold* button and I covered the X-bot in honey … it short circuited!"

"Great! Start your waggle dances."

"Green Grass One?" There was no reply. "Ant? What's going on?" Max called out again. Silence.

Finally, Ant's desperate voice called out, "Max? Max, I can't shake the X-bot! I've pushed all the buttons but … I can't hold it off much longer!"

Max looked at the real bees all gathered together around him. The waggle dance was over. It had worked. He took control of his machine again.

"Hold on, Ant," said Max, determined. "We're coming to get you!"

Max went at maximum speed towards the exit.

He flew up to the second level, hundreds of bees swarming behind him. There, he joined Cat. Together they flew up to the third level where they met Tiger. Then they all flew to the upper level of the hive. Behind them the bees massed.

Ant was trapped in a corner. The X-bot guard hovered over him. It moved into a striking position, just as Max, Cat and Tiger approached.

"Quick," shouted Max. "Surround him."

The air vibrated as Max, Cat, Tiger and the bees flew over to where Ant was cornered. The X-bot guard turned its metallic head. It was surrounded by the rest of Team X and an army of real bees. Max was sure he saw a look of fear flash in its red eyes. The X-bot dropped its sting, turned and fled.

The children's cheer was drowned out by the roar of buzzing from the bees.

"Let's get out of here," shouted a grateful Ant.

With that, Team X led the bees out into the bright sunshine of the African desert.

GREENVILLE NEWS

Can It Bee A Miracle?

Bee keepers across the globe are today celebrating after the mysterious return of all the missing bees. Over night, the sky was filled with swarms of bees all returning home. Nobody has an explanation. It seems as though the disaster predicted by Albert Einstein has been averted.

Motherwell Gets Gold

Today Rita Motherwell has been awarded a Golden Honey Pot for her organic honey at the Golden Honey Awards – the beekeepers' equivalent of the Oscars.

Find out more ...

For more **endangered** adventures, read *Piranha!*

And find out more about humans in danger in *Facing Danger*.

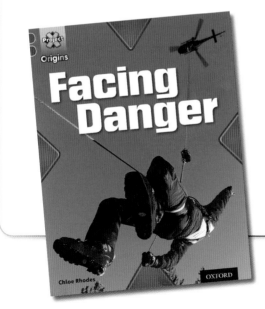